**This book is to be returned o
the last date stamped l**

LIBREX

Calendula (marigold) blossom opening

MEDICINE
FOR THE
WHOLE PERSON

A Guide to Anthroposophical Treatment

Dr Geoffrey Douch

Floris Books

First published in 2004 by Floris Books

© 2004 Floris Books

British Library CIP Data available

ISBN 0-86315-362-3

Printed in Poland

CONTENTS

ANTHROPOSOPHICAL MEDICINE

Origins of anthroposophical medicine

It is impossible to talk about anthroposophical medicine without at least mentioning anthroposophy. The founder of anthroposophy was Rudolf Steiner, who lived between 1861 and 1925, a time when the foundations of modern medicine were being laid down. Modern medical treatment only began a few years after his death, with the discovery of insulin, the advent of antibiotics, tranquillizers and hypnotics and, more recently, anti-inflammatory and immunosuppressive drugs, chemotherapy, radiotherapy and so on.

Developments in treatment came from ideas already inherent in the basic theories of pathology, which advocated that to understand why people became ill it was first necessary to understand why cells became ill. Steiner believed that this approach was of limited value, and emphasized that if medicine was not to degenerate into something purely mechanical, then doctors needed to understand how a person's soul and spirit affect the formation and function of the physical body.

The threefold image of the human body

An important principle of anthroposophical medicine is the three-fold structure of the human being as seen in the physical differences of the head, chest and limbs. The processes active within the threefold structure need to be balanced for good health.

The nerve-sense system is primarily located within the head, where coolness, stillness and quiet reign. The brain is well-protected inside the skull, but reacts badly to violent movement, for the nervous system has little possibility of regenerating damaged tissue. We find white and grey matter in the brain, not the varying colours of the intestines or other organs. We speak admiringly of someone who retains a 'cool head' in a stressful situation, and refer to an impulsive person as a 'hot head,' indicating the need of the nervous system for coolness.

The metabolic/limb system is the area of warmth, movement and noise. Here we see obvious limb movements as well as internal movements of

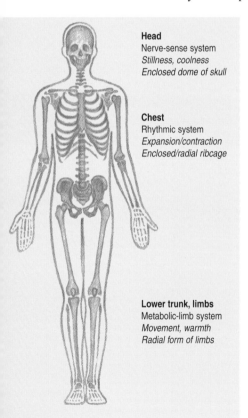

Head
Nerve-sense system
Stillness, coolness
Enclosed dome of skull

Chest
Rhythmic system
Expansion/contraction
Enclosed/radial ribcage

Lower trunk, limbs
Metabolic-limb system
Movement, warmth
Radial form of limbs

digestion which encompass the enormous, almost violent activity of breaking down foodstuffs, and also an active blood supply which increases after a good meal. The metabolic region is particularly full of life; for instance, the liver has the capacity to regenerate up to two-thirds of its substance when damaged by accident or disease. In many languages the word liver indicates the connection with life.

The central, rhythmic system keeps the balance between the metabolic/limb system and the nerve/sense systems. Its movements are manifest in the tireless contractions and expansions of the heart, and the regular movements of the ribcage during respiration.

These relationships are also clearly revealed in the skeleton: the enclosing dome of the skull contrasts with the progressive extensions of the limb bones, and in-between the rhythmic alternation of the ribcage which is partly open and partly closed.

In illness the balance between upper and lower pole is disturbed. The middle system becomes overextended in its role as mediator, as is shown by disturbances of pulse and respiration.

Relationship of body, soul and spirit

Anthroposophy encompasses a way of seeing and understanding the person in terms of an eternal and evolving spirit, as well as a soul that accompanies us as long as we are living in our bodies. Anthroposophical doctors perform routine consultations — in a way similar to other doctors' consultations — but many require a more in-depth exploration. This includes a particular interest in understanding how the body, soul and spiritual elements relate to one another.

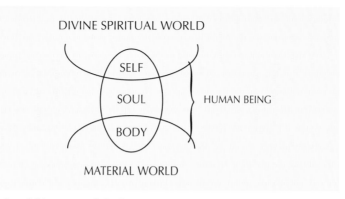

The threefold nature of the human being

The body includes what anthroposophists call the *physical* and the *etheric* body. The soul is associated with the *astral* body, and the spirit with the conscious individual self, or ego. These four elements work together in their different ways, and to a large extent determine our constitution, predisposition to illness and even our approach to life.

The manner and character of growth and development at different ages may also be important. Of course, all doctors recognize the importance of these questions in their own right, but it is unusual to ask these questions in order to understand why someone develops a particular illness at a particular stage in their biography (see page 13).

Kingdom of nature	Human element	State	Natural element
Human	Self, ego	Warmth	Fire
Animal	Astral (soul) body	Gas	Air
Plant	Etheric (life) body	Liquid	Water
Mineral	Physical body	Solid	Earth

Fourfold aspects of the human body

Even the physical body is ultimately shaped by the formative principles and laws which are found in the spiritual world, and which are not to be found purely in the material world. Anthroposophy includes the principle of reincarnation, maintaining that the human being has more than one life on this planet. We all therefore exist in a process of evolution and development, not purely in the Darwinian sense, but in a much wider context. An illness in one life can thus have profound consequences for how a person may be able to undertake his or her task in a following life. Illnesses therefore cease to be something whose meaning is defined only in terms of the present. This is particularly true of chronic and life-threatening illnesses, when this understanding can have a very real effect on the way a doctor engages with a patient. If illness is not merely viewed as a negative breakdown, but as having a positive aspect, then the doctor may treat certain conditions in ways that would not otherwise be considered, and also affect the patients' relationship to their illness in a positive way.

Conventional medicine treats the person as if the human body behaves according to the laws of the inorganic world. It studies the human body from the point of view of structure and function. The predominant idea is that the body is a mechanism, and thus influences the way doctors regard illness. Often, the laws of physics and chemistry are applied to the body, but the human aspect is reduced to the doctor trying to be pleasant and understanding. Although a good thing in its own right, it does not effectively improve the type of medicine that is being practised. The real potential of anthroposophical medicine is its ability to treat the person as more than the product of mechanical cause and effect. Anthroposophical doctors can therefore treat the patient inherently differently, considering all elements of the different bodies which make up a person.

During the historical development of anthroposophical medicine this was particularly true in the field of children with special needs. Anthroposophical doctors were actively involved in the education and treatment of such children from the 1920s onwards, developing many new medicines and artistic therapies: music, painting and eurythmy (see page 34). Subsequently, many other therapies were developed, such as massage and hydrotherapy, which build on and complement conventional medical methods.

The nature of disease

When a patient consults an anthroposophical practitioner the first question generally considered is whether the disease is of a more inflammatory, feverish nature, or a more sclerotic, degenerative kind. The majority of illnesses are predominantly inflammatory or sclerotic. In some illnesses, however, both elements may occur together. Childhood illnesses are more often inflammatory, while illnesses of old age are more commonly degenerative and sclerotic.

Most people treat illness as a negative experience or something that is best eliminated. An anthroposophical doctor assesses the 'value' of the condition. There is nothing terribly positive in sclerosis of any kind, be it arteriosclerosis, bone degeneration, osteoporosis, osteoarthritis, cataracts, gallstones, and so on. However, illnesses that have a feverish component, particularly those that run a clearly defined course, for example,

characteristic childhood illnesses such as measles, are poten-
tially productive and important in terms of anthroposophical
medicine. If a child contracts measles their normal life processes
are completely disrupted; the child is sad and withdrawn. This is
followed by convalescence, when the child's normal life condition is restored and psychological depression disappears. However, in the two or three months after measles the child's
physical and psychological development often accelerates dramatically, more rapidly than during the year before the illness.
This is especially noticeable in special-needs children who have
suffered from such a childhood disease; their development progresses substantially during the period of convalescence. Medical studies have also found that children who were not
vaccinated against measles and who later developed the illness
fully, not only have a stronger immune system for the future, but
also have a lower incidence of cancer and degenerative bone disease in later life, than those who do not develop measles fully.

The importance of biography

The term *biography* literally means a living script. Just as any
great piece of music will display a particular structure within a
time signature, similar structures can always be found in the
way that a life is *composed*.

There is a pattern of seven-year rhythms, which is easy to see
in childhood. The first phase is 0–7, and 7–14 and 14–21 are
very clear and distinct following phases. We see this rhythm con-
tinuing right up until old age, and often crises or transition
points happen near or around such developmental stages. For

instance, 28, 35, 42, 49, and 56 are often transition points in life. Broadly speaking, our lives have three phases: an exposition phase in which the basic aspects of our biography evolve, which spans the first three seven-year periods of development; a middle phase in which these themes are developed and evolve, from 21 until about the age of 42, and finally, there is a phase in which the individual may achieve an increasing measure of freedom with respect to the given factors of his or her development. This does not happen as a matter of course, but requires active creative participation, sometimes with the help of a doctor or therapist. These three phases are seen to correspond with the development of body, soul and spirit.

Experiences in the earlier seven year periods may find a recapitulation in later seven-year phases, sometimes bearing a relationship to particular illnesses.

Certain types of education where, at an early age, intellectual elements are emphasized at an early age to the detriment of artistic factors, may contribute to a predisposition to more sclerotic illnesses after the age of 42. It is of course realized in general psychology that experiences during the formative years of child development leave a deep and lasting imprint on the personality. What is less readily appreciated is the impact of psychological experiences on the body. The younger we are the more direct this impact is. Shocks or traumatic experiences in childhood may lead

Period	Developmental mode	Cultural orientation	Attribute
1–7	Will	Religion	Goodness
7–14	Feeling	Art	Beauty
14–21	Thinking	Science	Truth

to chronic problems with digestion in later life, eg, a tendency to stomach ulcers or irritable bowel syndrome. Fear may disturb patterns of sleep and affect our manner of breathing. This in turn may affect the circulation, influencing heart rhythms and so on. In making an in-depth assessment of a patient's condition it is helpful to ascertain the underlying factors which have contributed to the symptoms, whether they are at the physical level, or on the level of the etheric or astral body. This in turn contributes to a more meaningful and differentiated diagnostic picture which in turn influences the kind of treatment needed.

Treatment

It is necessary in any therapeutic relationship, that a developing sense of trust and confidence emerges between patient and doctor or therapist. However, there is a difference between feeling confident and actually believing in a certain philosophy. A patient's commitment to a particular treatment undoubtedly influences the outcome of the treatment. However, many factors may contribute to that commitment. As such, special beliefs are not required at all, any more than for any other form of medicine. It is important, however, to always appeal to common sense, and to establish confidence in the doctor or therapist.

There are many doctors in general practice using anthroposophically developed medicines with patients who take them purely because their doctor regards them as the best medicine for them. These patients often seem to benefit particularly well. This points to the importance of the relationship between doctor and patient.

The therapeutic approach

Although it encompasses conventional medical practice, anthroposophical medicine differs from it in its development of complementary therapies. *Massage* and *hydrotherapy* techniques have evolved which are obviously body orientated. Then there is a whole spectrum of *artistic therapies* which stimulate the patient to participate consciously in a process of development offered by challenges of the artistic medium. At first, the results may not be noticeable, but after weeks or months the patient becomes aware that something has been taking place that they were not initially aware of, so their own conscious participation will be encouraged.

Then there is also the *counselling* or *psychotherapeutic* aspect. This has much in common with present-day psychology but also offers additional perspectives on human development, and includes the hypothesis that we have more than one life on earth, and various thoughts on the phases of human development.

Finally we come to the medicines themselves. Some of these are drawn from herbal, traditional or homoeopathic medicines. Others are brought together in pharmaceutical processes that are specific to anthroposophical pharmacy. Viscum preparations for example belong to this group. They are based on mistletoe, and are used primarily in the treatment of cancer (see page 50).

THERAPIES

Anthroposophical nursing

All nurses working with anthroposophical medicine are first and foremost qualified nurses with state registration. In addition to the skills required of a registered nurse, the anthroposophical nurse also works with herbal teas and decoctions (see page 48), for compresses, inhalations and therapeutic baths with healing plants such as ginger, mustard, lemon or onions in poultices and packs; with plant and metal ointments and oils for *Einreibung* — a form of gentle rhythmical massage unique to anthroposophical nursing.

This large repertoire of nursing treatments as well as the extensive *materia medica* of anthroposophical medicines gives the nurse a great deal of variety, and to some extent autonomy and choice in their daily care. While medicines and therapeutic treatments are prescribed by the doctor, certain remedies can be given at the discretion of the experienced nurse for common ailments such as headaches, flu-like symptoms, insomnia or indigestion. Thus someone suffering from insomnia will not

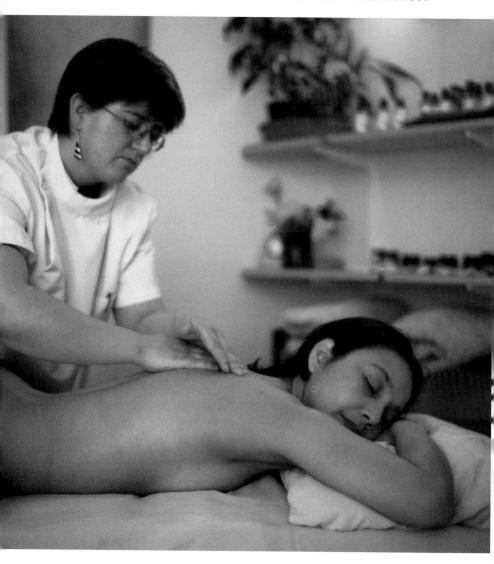

Einreibung massage

automatically receive a prescription dose of Temazepam, but depending on the nature of the insomnia will receive a treatment or anthroposophical remedy specific to their need.

For example, the nurse may ask whether the patient has difficulty falling asleep due to uncontrollable, anxious thoughts? Does the patient regularly wake between 3 and 4 am, unable to return to sleep again? Perhaps the patient finds it difficult to wake up in the morning, only seeming to come alive in the evening with the resultant difficulty in finding calm at night?

Even if the sleep problem is not the main cause for the patient's current treatment, lack of, or disturbed sleep will inevitably interfere with the overall healing process. The experienced anthroposophical nurse aims to improve the patient's sleep pattern with a choice of therapeutic possibilities ranging from a calming herbal tea, an evening footbath with lavender, a morning footbath with rosemary, a chamomile abdominal compress or an *Einreibung* massage to the back, arms or legs with an appropriate oil. In addition, there are several anthroposophical medicines for different types of sleep disturbance. The observation of the nurse and their knowledge and experience of anthroposophical treatments enables them to make an appropriate choice for each patient's needs. It should be noted, however, that a chronic sleep problem would be referred to a doctor and a comprehensive treatment plan prescribed accordingly.

Many of the external treatments given by anthroposophical nurses are not new, in fact they are often considered to be old-fashioned. What is new, however, is the theory behind their use. This comes from an understanding of the human as a being of body, soul and spirit as described by Rudolf Steiner.

Part of a nurse's further study therefore includes more advanced consideration of the human being in health and illness, as well as plant observations and studies of other natural substances in order to learn about their healing properties.

Einreibung is a treatment unique to anthroposophical medicine, and relates predominantly to the healing, balancing potential of the middle system. It is a refined form of massage. It works by bringing a type of healing, breathing quality to the body, and can be used in several ways: to bring a prescribed substance to the body or as a preventative measure, for example, for pressure sores, or to treat a specific problem, such as anxiety or sleep disturbance. It pervades all areas of nursing, influencing how the nurse washes or even moves a patient.

Anthroposophical nursing strives to work holistically, recognizing the individual not only as a physical/spiritual being, but also as a person with their own unique biography. Nurses generally come into contact with the individual as a patient; someone who is ill or experiencing a life crisis. Looking at the illness in relation to the person's life as a whole makes it possible to find meaning in the illness, to view it as a possible challenge or opportunity for change and growth, rather than an undesirable event to be suppressed, removed or denied at all costs.

As in any conventional medical setting, it is usually the nurse who has the most intimate and continuous contact with the patient. The nurse's view of the individual as described will also influence the nature of the nurse-patient relationship, and how to accompany an individual through illness and suffering to acceptance. Many diseases cannot be cured, but an individual's ability to learn to live with, and accept, their illness as part of themselves and their destiny, can bring about a state of inner

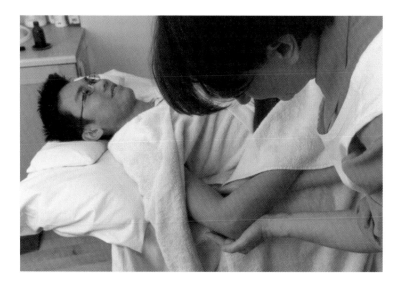

Rhythmical massage

health and well-being, regardless of physical or mental pain, or disablement.

Many diseases of the body have their origin in the soul, and many 'soul conditions' or psychiatric illnesses have their root in the physical body. Thus the nurse working with anthroposophical medicine may find him or herself treating a psychiatric disorder by applying a mustard compress to the kidneys, or listening to and counselling someone with cancer.

Perhaps more than in conventional medicine, in anthroposophical medicine nurses share their observations of the patient more closely with doctors and other therapists, as the multidisciplinary approach is given priority. Not only physical medical observations are shared, but the nurse, together with the other health-care professionals, strives to gain a deep understanding of each patient and the purpose of their illness, in order to help them achieve a state of equilibrium and well-being.

The nurse's role, as part of the therapeutic team, is to walk alongside the patient, accompanying them through this stage of their biography; whether it is long-standing depression, convalescing after surgery, coming to terms with a diagnosis, or living the last days of their life. The nurse endeavours to support the individual in finding some freedom in relation to their illness. Accompanying individuals through illness, pain and suffering requires more than just practical skills. It is possible to acquire inner strength and the ability to care and show compassion without losing oneself, or feeling drained. The aim is to enable patients to work creatively with their illness, helping the patient to participate in the process. This is an active process which has a profound effect on the nurse too, and a commitment to deepening self-knowledge is essential.

Rhythmical massage

Rythmical Massage aids the body's self-healing abilities. It gives the individuals' better control of their body, rectifying imbalances derived from stress and/or illness, thus supporting and restoring the body's own harmony and healing.

Rhythm is central to healthy life processes. The masseur/euse can strengthen or calm either one of the two major functional activities of the body; those associated with the nervous system, or those active in the metabolism. The practitioner is even able to address aspects of the causes of illness, by seeking to strengthen the process of self-healing.

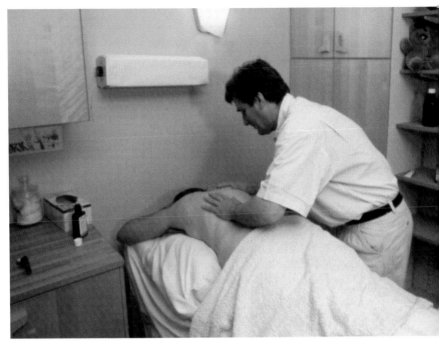

Rhythmical massage

The therapist often works on one part of the body in order to influence another. For example, a concentration of tension and warmth in the head, neck and shoulders is often accompanied by coldness and tension usually in the lower body, especially thighs, calves and feet. Rhythmical massage aims to bring warmth and tonus to the lower half of the body, while also working to relieve tension in the upper body, thus harmonizing the interrelationship of these two polarities.

One of the most important techniques is one in which the principles of strengthening and loosening are rhythmically alternated, like the breathing rhythm or heart beat. This is, in essence, a form of kneading; beginning with a gentle, warm dipping-in, using very little pressure, and taking hold of the soft tissue and then using a pulling action with either one or both hands of the practitioner. This quality enables the life processes within the tissues to be stimulated and enlivened. The tissues are thus lifted out of weight and into lightness. Another important movement integral to this massage is that of the *lemniscate* (figure of eight), applied in various ways.

The external stimulation of massage needs to be absorbed by the body. So following a massage session there is a rest period of about twwenty minutes to allow the body to absorb and integrate the beneficial effects of the treatment. This facilitates a response, which takes place mainly during the night following the massage.

In most treatments a variety of oils are used, to address and stimulate the warmth organism and the functional three-foldness of the human being (see pages 8–10). A fatty carrier oil (such as sunflower seed oil) is used as a basis, and ethereal oils (made from plant extracts), and other remedial substances are added. In general we can relate the parts of the plant to the different elements of the human being. For example, the roots of plants act upon the formative nerve-sense processes which are predominant in the head. The realm of leaves relates to respiration and circulation. Blossom substances are associated with the more sulphurous activities of the metabolic region (see page 46). Seeds hold the essence of the complete plant in them, thus addressing the integrity of the whole.

Rhythmical massage is suitable for children, adults and the

elderly; it is particularly beneficial in the treatment of acute and chronic conditions, such as:

— orthopaedic conditions like joint replacements, fractures, rheumatoid arthritis, osteoporosis;
— circulatory problems such as oedema, high and low blood pressure, and related disorders;
— pain management; muscle tension, strains and sprains;
— certain aspects of cancer treatment;
— psychological conditions such as stress, anxiety/depression, emotional trauma;
— immune deficiencies, and many other conditions.

Rhythmical massage therapy was developed by Dr Ita Wegman in the 1920s. In addition to her medical training she was also schooled in physiotherapy and remedial massage (classical Swedish massage). She established a clinic in Switzerland with Rudolf Steiner where anthroposophical medicine was first practised, and here they developed this new approach to remedial massage together with Dr Margarethe Hauschka. They also developed some aspects of hydrotherapy with a series of 'movement' baths, which are in effect a form of water massage.

Hydrotherapy

Within anthroposophical medicine, various types of hydrotherapy are being used and developed — for example, arm and foot baths as well as whole body baths, which use herbal and mineral extracts treated in a variety of ways before being added to the bath water. Movement baths, being a form of water massage, are also employed. Brushes of various types can be used, depending on the condition and type of person one is treating. Water is the medium through which the etheric life forces work, and therefore has a special connection with healing processes inherent in the body.

Aromatic oils are also employed in a unique form of therapeutic bath known as the *Oil Dispersion Bath.* Oil is finely dispersed throughout the water rather than floating on the surface (achieved by the use of an ingenious piece of equipment, the Jungebad apparatus). The resultant marriage of oil and water interacts with the skin and is rapidly absorbed by the body, unfolding its warming, healing qualities. Slight though measurable increases in body temperature can be recorded even when the bath temperature is lower than that of the body; many people find this most relaxing and often drift into a light but refreshing sleep.

When applying anything warm or hot to body tissue, the muscles relax and blood vessels open more widely. It is generally considered better not to get directly into a hot bath as this causes an extreme form of vasodilation, and an enormous amount of extra energy is expended just to come back to oneself, to 'be centred' again; if one really has the wish and need to be 'warmed through', it is advisable to get into a mildly warm bath and gradually raise the water temperature by adding small amounts of hot water while in it.

Cold causes hardening, a contraction gesture, often experienced as quite refreshing. A balanced interplay of these characteristics can decrease congestion and increase general circulation.

The primary effect of hydrotherapy is on bodily functions, such as circulation, muscle tone and the general distribution and integrity of the warmth organism. The therapeutic potential of baths has been recognized for centuries, and now there are a variety of hydrotherapy treatments which can be applied by an anthroposophical practitioner.

Music therapy

The range of activities grouped under the music therapy umbrella is very diverse. What distinguishes anthroposophical music therapy from others is the creative and central role played by an anthroposophical understanding of music and the human being. Particular musical-therapeutic strategies are used in

Music eurythmy therapy

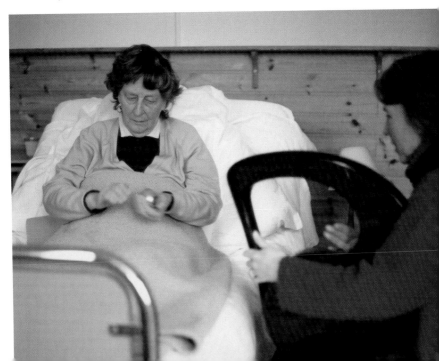

medicine, education and special needs education. Unusual instruments such as modern additions to the lyre family as well as recently-developed string, wind and percussion instruments complement an underlying understanding of music and its working on people.

The patient experiences music in the feeling realm. For example, the major tones convey a feeling of outward radiance, while the minor intervals awaken an inward-turning warmth. Music steers towards wholeness and harmony, and feelings are experienced in new clarity. A new awareness and a sense of balance can enter the patient's life.

The particular music therapy develops from the life situation of the patient, affects the choice of instrument and whether the therapy should be individual or group-orientated. Depending on the patient the music may be composed or improvised, and music-making or listening may be emphasized. What matters is the process, not a fine performance. Modest music can bring healing, a sense of wellbeing and inner progress.

Music therapy helps create a sense of peace and security. It can relax the ageing mind that is struggling against the onset of dementia, soothe the fears of the terminally ill, or calm the behaviour of the emotionally disturbed child. It can help disturbed adolescents, as well as allowing individuals to balance loneliness by actively participating in a musical community. It will strengthen self-confidence and self-respect.

Art therapy

Anthroposophical art therapy works with the active involvement of the individual in their own healing process. Through painting, drawing and sculpture initial exploratory sessions can lead to a path of therapy. This may involve aspects of nature and the world around us — summer, winter, sunrise, sunset — or more individually, our inner life of feeling and imagination. In both cases a living world of form and colour is engaged, and our creativity is awakened and mobilized.

In *drawing*, charcoal can be used and the polarities of light and darkness explored. The challenge may be to bring these two extremes into harmony, or to lead the light into the darkness. Such exercises can bring courage and strength and boost a patient's self-confidence.

Art therapy

In *painting* there are many approaches although watercolour is the preferred medium. For instance, in the exercises 'forming and dissolving' a copy is made of a reproduction, and then in a series of paintings the forms and the colours can be altered and freed. Out of the resulting colour dynamic a new motif is achieved. This brings movement, helping to free any tendency to inflexibility, and at the same time stimulates imagination and the capacity for transformation.

The experience of the inherent qualities of colour is important in painting therapy. The expansive and awakening qualities of yellow, the warmth of red or the sheltering qualities of blue are just some of the many possibilities offered by the world of colour.

Supported by the therapist on this creative journey, obstacles can be overcome and one-sidedness balanced out. Processes of renewal are encouraged, not only mentally, but also on the body. Areas such as pulse, blood pressure and breathing can be helped through the use of specific colours, themes or methods of working. Not least an active involvement in their own path of healing can bring a new-found sense of purpose and freedom into the patients' life.

Sculpture therapy

Sculpture therapy is used particularly in situations where patients have difficulty focusing and concentrating, or have behavioural disturbances. Such situations might result from depression, anxiety and life crises, as well as from cancer, high blood pressure, eczema and chronic fatigue syndrome.

As with painting and drawing, a wide range of exercises are

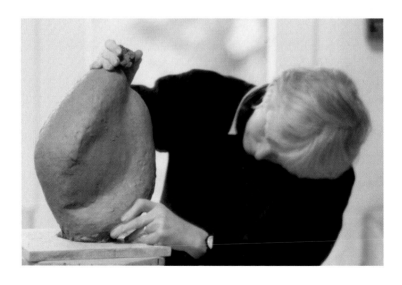

possible. Initially, diagnostic exercises are given, either with the therapist working alongside the patient making a ball out of clay, or with the patient being given some clay and asked to do a free exercise. The therapist gets to know the patient and the way they work with the material, observing how they express themselves in form. During the following sessions the therapist is able to work more constructively with the patient and suggest forms or exercises which best enable the patient to meet the experiences and challenges that they need for their own healing. For example, the therapist may suggest an angular, geometric shape to focus the concentration, or a rounded, smooth form to calm anxiety.

As treatment progresses more substantial forms may be made with the patient standing and working at a sculpture stand. Such exercises may use basic sculptural concepts as their starting point, such as uprightness, the opposition of weightlessness and gravity, or the contrast between expansion and contraction. Alternatively, the patient may be set a theme exercise, based on peacefulness or determination. Other exercises may consist of types of dialogue, or a series of sculptures that develops and undergoes transformation. In this way the patient is challenged by artistic sensitivity and activity. Wood and stone carving can also be introduced as appropriate.

Sculpture therapy can be used as often as four times a week, in 45-minute sessions, or can be stretched over several months with a single one-hour session per week providing continuity.

In sculpture therapy healing can be fostered in a number of ways and at different levels. For example:
- Interested and enthusiastic involvement in and creating with a new medium can lead to finding new possibilities of expression.
- It can challenge crises of self-confidence, low self-image or self-doubt.
- The shape and character of the form itself can work directly on qualities of wakefulness, concentration and breathing.
- The possibilities inherent in sculptural form and movement can reveal new ways of thinking and reacting to situations.
- Sculpture can provide security by means of its substantiality, the limitations of the medium and integrity of expression.

Eurythmy therapy

Eurythmy is a form of movement of the body which reflects sounds both of music (tone eurythmy) and speech (speech eurythmy). It was created by Rudolf Steiner as a result of his studies into the nature of the human being.

The forces of movement in nature and the universe are inherent in the human organism, both visibly and invisibly. Our soul moves in response to the changing seasons, to music, or to a stimulating conversation. Through eurythmy we discover healing properties and are guided to transform our habits, attitudes and the body.

In eurythmy therapy the patients take an active, conscious step in transforming their condition. The ingrained patterns of nutrition, posture, unrhythmical lifestyle and inner attitudes which have created the imbalance are harmonized and rebalanced in the practice of therapeutic eurythmy.

After meeting the patient and observing simple movements the eurythmy therapist decides on an initial course of treatment, choosing a specific sequence of movements for that particular individual. The sessions occur on a one-to-one basis, for a minimum of thirty minutes a week, over an average of seven to ten sessions. A child could have as little as twenty minutes preferably twice a week.

The therapist does not use manipulation but teaches through instruction and demonstration. Many movements are based on sounds of speech or elements of music. The patient is then encouraged to practise these exercises for ten to twenty minutes daily.

Eurythmy can be applied to many illnesses, including sclerotic and nervous disorders, asthma and allergies, heart, blood and cancerous conditions. It can be given before and after operations, thereby accelerating the healing process, and can help in overcoming paralysis, speech impediments, eye problems, drug addiction and depression. Special exercises can also be given for dyslexia, coordination, concentration and memory. Treatment can complement conventional medicine.

Therapeutic speech

Therapeutic speech is an artistic therapy developed from speech formation, an art of speaking renewed by Rudolf Steiner and Marie Steiner-von Sievers at the beginning of the twentieth century. Using the anthroposophical image of the human being as its basis, speech formation has led to new forms of recitation and drama.

In the artistic process, speech formation works with and develops elements such as rhythm, content, breath and sound quality to grasp the soul-spiritual content of poetry and express it accordingly. In therapy these elements help to overcome imbalances in the speech of children and adults which result from pathological disorders. The therapist tries to achieve this by harmonizing the process of speaking itself, and by working with the therapeutic forces of sounds and speech elements.

When a person becomes ill the imbalance in the person's life processes expresses itself as an imbalance in the speech — for example, poor or over articulation, incorrect breathing or a disorder in the voice often accompanies illness.

Therapeutic speech offers a way of treating the areas of imbalance through speech exercises involving articulation, breath, fluency and voice adjustment. The exercises are combined with rhythms, movements and gestures. In this way the particular sound of a word becomes full of creative, living force.

Poetry also finds its place in the therapeutic process, bringing elements such as rhythm, sound combinations and content. Poetry expresses two fundamental relationships to the world:

one is reciting remembered events; the other is expressing (declaiming) one's feelings to the world. These two types of poetry — recitation and declamation — require opposite techniques of breathing by the individual, and may be used to address imbalances in constitutional disorders. For instance, during recitation the speech becomes rounded and warm, while during declamation the speech becomes radiating and directed.

The therapist does not draw attention to breath. The exhalation required by a particular sequence of words is the determining factor for deeper inhalation. Also, the imagination is urged to breathe in 'pictures' during the in-breath to give the necessary strength for the sounds and rhythms to the out-breath. This way of breathing in encourages picture building in the imagination, and is experienced as refreshing and enlivening.

Thus, therapeutic speech is not only a way of treating language and speech disorders but it can also deal specifically with a broad range of illnesses from internal and general medicine as well as psychosomatics, psychiatry and special needs, since it is based on a therapeutic process, deeply influencing the relationship between body, soul and spirit.

Speech therapists train full-time for four years which includes practical periods in clinics, medical practices, special needs schools or social therapy settings.

Biographical counselling

At times we all feel overwhelmed with what life throws into our lap — we may face obstacles and breakdowns in our relationships, illness, bereavement, fear of death, crisis and stress, or deep, unresolved questions about ourselves and our path in life. Any one of these can stir responses in our souls which are so confusing, painful or paralysing that we feel as though we have been taken over by circumstance and emotion. Staying in control becomes our chief goal which we attempt by busying ourselves with issues of duty, work and routine. Our hurt and anger drives us to compulsive avoidance of the core issues. There are also times when we can find ourselves emotionally bereft, lethargic, impotent and spiritually empty. It is very draining trying to tame and live with these reactions especially as we frequently use highly sophisticated, often destructive patterns of thinking.

Biographical counselling offers an opportunity to share circumstances, issues and responses in a safe environment with someone who is trained as a counsellor, and who is familiar with the dynamics and laws at work in our biographies. In this setting the patient can begin to find new perspectives and connect with a source of renewed creativity and strength. Through shared exploration, it is possible to pick up the threads of life with refreshed energy and purpose, to reconnect with our inner being and gain insights that can strengthen acceptance and work with the situations and gestures of our lives.

In a process of counselling our awareness can move through the outer complexities of our circumstances, to our thoughts, feelings and instinctive reactions, and then towards a deeper and more conscious connection between our day-to-day self and the self we are searching for.

The rhythms, patterns of development, laws and dynamics that are at work in our body, soul and spirit can be useful tools in this process. They can help us recognize where we are in our journey, and the inner nature of our questions and dilemmas and the wider context of their relationship with the evolution of humanity. Through this exploration, we can begin to recognize our individual self — our very personal stamp, quest and destiny.

Acceptance, loss, fear, doubt and pain feature in many of our inner experiences, all of which can become unconscious dictators of our reactions. Having the opportunity to acknowledge and work with these issues helps render them less powerful so that new, creative responses can be tried: reactions can change to response, patterns to risk-taking and initiative. Developing the ability to live for the moment, disentangled from the patterns of the past and with courage for the future, is the hallmark of creativity. Biographical counselling is an opportunity to begin, or deepen, the process of weaving the strands of our life together with meaningful and renewed warmth and enthusiasm.

Biography work in groups

As human beings we share certain questions which initially arise when we enter puberty and accompany us into old age. Where have we come from? What are we here for? Why are certain things happening to me, those close to me and in the world at large? Who am I?

Biography work attempts to find answers to these questions by researching lives in a group setting; in order to develop a sense for perceiving our individuality working within us, expressing itself through our body in a physical way, as well as manifesting itself through our biographies over our lifetimes.

For instance, Rudolf Steiner recognized that the experience of a nine-year-old can influence and rule the deeds and feelings of a thirty-year-old, and so on. He advised a way of extracting ourselves from these experiences by making an objective picture of the incidents, events, meetings which we have undergone, looking at ourselves as if we were someone else. In this way we distance ourselves from the event. The outcome is an emancipation from our experiences, which leaves us free to observe rather than identify with our experiences, which can cause us to feel trapped by them.

When we do this kind of work with even seemingly insignificant life events, we end up with a gallery of pictures which gradually reveals something of our innermost nature, our true being. It opens our eyes to the forces which have worked to create our biography from inside as well as from the outside. It allows us to see our biography as a whole, including the present and yet unknown future, and to find the golden thread which weaves through the tapestry of our life.

Looked at from this angle biography work does not seem a very social activity although its benefit for the individual may be recognized. And yet the fact that it is done in a group changes the work dramatically.

Apart from sharing our own biography, we listen to the biographies of other people. We are asked not to comment, interpret or analyse but to give space and attention to another human being. Practising nonjudgemental listening, and holding back our opinions, trains our faculties of observation and objectivity. Therefore, the picture of our shared lives finally starts to speak to us rather than us speaking aloud.

In biography workshops this is done in groups of four so that by listening to the pictures of another's life, one's own life becomes more visible and gains in uniqueness and character. It usually consists of three elements: facilitated groupwork, talks on the development of the individual, and artistic work.

REMEDIES

Research and production

Anthroposophical remedies are based on the philosophy that humans should live in harmony with nature. Consequently, one of the central values of a manufacturer such as Weleda or Wala, is the pursuit of health without exploiting natural resources. A conscious responsibility towards the environment underlies every detail of the operation, from the organic raising of plants to the final packaging, made from recycled materials or from managed, sustainable sources. Anthroposophical medicines make use of man's relationship to the mineral, plant and animal kingdoms, from which they are prepared. Their action is based upon the fourfold nature of the human body, and the interrelationships of bodily, soul and spiritual activities within the human organism. This interaction determines the balance between health and illness.

The medicines were originally developed in the 1920s, as an extension to the conventional medicines available to them. Since that time, a wide range of other products, such as skin and body-care products, has been developed (without animal testing). The

Biodynamically grown phacelia

ingredients of both the medicines and other goods are selected for their natural therapeutic properties. Traditional manufacturing methods and ingredients exist alongside stringent quality controls and modern pharmaceutical technology.

Most healing substances are found in the natural world, and how and where they are applied to the body is of great relevance. Different metals have a relationship both to the planets and to certain organs of the body. The parts of the plant also correspond to different parts of the body, and it is important whether the root, stem, leaves or blossom are used. It is also significant whether a healing substance is given by mouth into the digestive system, externally through a sensory organ such as the skin, or injected into a muscle or the blood stream.

Wherever possible, the plants and herbs are grown by the

Metal	Planet	Working on	Related organs
Lead	Saturn	⎫	Spleen, skeleton
Tin	Jupiter	Nerve-sense system	Liver
Iron	Mars	⎭	Gall, larynx
Gold	Sun	Rhythmic system	Heart
Copper	Venus		Kidney, ears
Mercury	Mercury	Metabolic-limb system	Lungs, eyes
Silver	Moon		Sexual organs, brain

The relationship of metals to the planets and to organs of the body

manufacturers themselves, free from artificial fertilizers or pesticides to ensure the finest and purest ingredients. Many are grown according to an organic method of cultivation called biodynamic agriculture. This method works with the natural rhythms of the seasons and takes account of the natural changes in light at different times of the month and day, when planting, cultivating or harvesting, in order to retain the maximum therapeutic properties of the plants.

Rudolf Steiner made a remarkable discovery about medicinal plants. He found that a plant with healing properties often has a distortion or abnormality in its proportions or make-up, compared with non-medicinal plants which are ideally proportioned. An ideal plant would have perfect harmony between flower, root and leaf, reflecting the three systems of the human being in

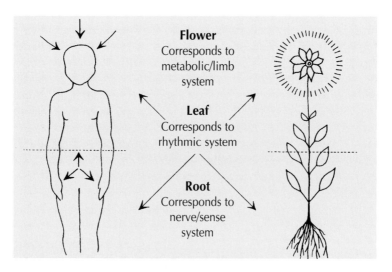

Correspondence between parts of plant and of human being

harmony when in health. In humans, an imbalance in these systems leads to illness, However, in plants, an imbalance between the three main parts reveals a healing quality.

Using the relationship of the plant to the systems of the body, plants are identified that can be used in anthroposophical medi-

---

D, X and C Potencies

In the process of dilution, usually one part extract to ten parts or one hundred parts of dilutent are taken and potentized. Ten part dilution is referred to as D or X, while hundred part is referred to as C potency. The number following the letter is the number of times the process has been repeated.

Thus, a D8 potency has been diluted as 1 to 10, eight times successively. The amount of original substance is now 1/100,000,000 part of the medicine.

---

cine, and specific parts of the plant are used to treat specific illnesses according to these relationships. Homeopathic remedies form a great part of anthroposophical medicines. In homeopathy, the symptoms of an illness are viewed as the body's attempt to heal itself. A medicine is therefore chosen, which is capable of producing similar symptoms if given to a well person. In this way, homeopathy tries to stimulate the body's own natural healing capacity, with homeopathic remedies acting as a trigger for the body's own ability to heal itself.

The preparation of a medicine is just as important as the choice of the substance itself. Methods of preparation are used which are designed to accentuate the substance's

Medicine preparation

therapeutic properties, and anthroposophical doctors work in close collaboration with pharmacists to develop appropriate methods. Traditional pharmaceutical and homeopathic techniques are used as well as new methods.

Many homeopathic remedies are made by the process of

Specific manufacturing processes

Decoction

An aqueaous/ethanol plant mixture is heated under reflux to boiling and then maintained at boiling for 30 minutes. After cooling it is allowed to stand in a closed container for 24 hours before pressing and filtration. Steam penetrates the substance and a reflux condensor is used to prevent the loss of volatile ingredients. It is especially suited to roots, to release their effect. The introduction of rigorous heat is used to orientate the substance towards the metabolic-limb system.

Oil extracts

Oil extracts are normally prepared from dried plants and extracted using a vegetable oil base (e.g. sunflower seed oil, olive oil). The extract can be prepared cold or with the introduction of a gentle heat. The oil is strained after a specified period to remove the plant residue. Oil extracts are used as a method of extracting plant materials into a non-alcoholic base for external application to the skin.

Digestion

The aqueous/ethanol plant mixture is heated to body temperature (37°C) and maintained at this temperature for 1 hour. After cooling, the mass is transformed to a suitable container, sealed and left for 14 days before it is pressed and filtered. This process is an orientation of the substance towards the human being (blood temperature) and is particularly useful when the plant is intended to work on the rhythmic system.

dilution and potentization. The starting material, usually a plant extract, is diluted with either water, or water and alcohol. The material is then *potentized*, that is rhythmically shaken, for a prescribed period of time, in order to release the energy within the substance. The process of dilution can be repeated until the desired potency is reached. In this way, infinitesimally small doses can be administered without undesirable side effects, and it has been found that these doses are more effective than larger doses.

Selected temperatures are also used in the preparation of medicines. In classical homeopathy medicines are made by finely chopping the material and mixing it with alcohol and water. The mixture is then allowed to stand in temperatures of below 20°C for at least five days before being filtered. This produces the mother tincture which is used to start off the process of potentization.

In anthroposophical practice, the temperature used to prepare a medicine depends upon the particular medicine. For example, aconite, which has cold qualities connected with the forces of the head, is prepared at a cool temperature. Birch leaves, used to overcome sclerosis, are prepared at around 90°C. Medicines with an affinity with the middle, rhythmic system are prepared at the average human body temperature of 37°C.

Anthroposophical medicines exist in many different forms, such as tablets, dilutions, injections, ointments, oils, powders, suppositories and lotions. The variety of products is mirrored by the range of manufacturing processes used to create these products, for example, decoctions, distillation, potentization, trituration, among others. At all times, purity and quality are maintained using every advantage of modern technology. The most modern analytical techniques and computerized equipment are utilized in quality control laboratories to produce a vast range of substances, from over-the-counter remedies to prescription-only medicines.

Often an anthroposophical doctor's prescription is highly individualized to reflect the particular spiritual and physical constitution of the patient. This is particularly the case when homeopathically potentized metals are prescribed. However, for certain conditions, the prescription is specific for a particular illness. For example, Combudoron for burns, and Avena Sativa for sleeplessness.

Medicines and their uses

Many of the medicines and remedies are developed for specific illnesses and disorders. The most well-known of these are Viscum preparations which are based on mistletoe *(Viscum album),* and used to stimulate the immune system, particularly for the treatment of cancer.

Mistletoe is a unique plant. It does not have the orientation of upper and lower parts, or between gravity and lightness as is usual in plants attached to the soil. Mistletoe grows perpendicular to the branch which bears it, increasing according to its own rhythm, and free from the conditions to which other plants must submit. It remains green all year round, independently of its exposure to the light. Its sucker even stores chlorophyll in the darkness of the wood where no light is found. Its berries ripen in winter without the help of natural warmth, and its leaves are indifferent to the orientation of the light and gravity.

As a result, mistletoe has freed itself from both earthly and sun forces, and thus has a very special place in the vegetable kingdom. It is possible to say that the plant rejects terrestrial forces, and therefore behaves in a manner which is opposite to a cancer which opens itself to them.

Viscum may be used in all forms of cancer and pre-cancerous conditions. It is capable of strengthening the body's defences against loss of form which is the result of cancer. The inflammatory processes resulting from treatment by Viscum which may be a rise in temperature or redness around the tumour or injection site, are signs that immunological processes have been stimulated.

By applying a medicinal substance as an external application to the body surface, it is possible to restore balance and in a sense, remind the bodily processes of where they belong.

An example is the use of a mustard footbath which in many cases can ward off an impending migraine. In migraines we see a situation where the metabolic processes have invaded the nerve/sense pole resulting in pain, nausea, vomiting, sometimes visual disturbances and light sensitivity — the peace and quiet of the head pole is literally shattered. Often, the patient's feet

Mistletoe – used to treat cancer

Lemon reduces inflammation

are cold. Finely ground black mustard seed *(Sinapis nigra)* is mixed with warm water (37°C). The patient then immerses his/her feet and lower legs for around 15 minutes. Care is taken that the patient is warm enough, and afterwards is allowed to rest in a quiet room, with no bright light. The mustard draws warmth to the lower body, so the metabolic processes are drawn away from the head. The substance appeals to the patients own physiological activity rather than simply removing the pain.

Another element of anthroposophical medicine is to observe substances in a way which reveals their therapeutic properties. For example, the lemon *(Citrus media)* quite readily reveals its properties. What is unusual about the fruit of the lemon is that even in its ripe state it remains sour. The tree, native to the tropics, is a contracted dense plant, with dark green, waxy leaves. Having produced fragrant, white flowers, the fruit (the metabolic pole of the plant) is sour not sweet, as well as compact, structured and bright yellow. Having absorbed the tropical sun the lemon stores it in an unusual way. Just thinking of the face one would pull after taking a large bite of lemon, gives us a clue about its qualities. Lemon is used for fever and inflammation, that is, to draw in and reduce overriding metabolic processes. A typical treatment for someone with a fever, whose extremities are warm would be to apply lemon compresses to the calves; or for a sore throat a lemon compress might be applied locally.

Common over-the-counter remedies

Arnica

The healing properties of the flower of this European mountain plant were known back in the sixteenth century. Arnica tablets are most commonly used as an emergency prevention to stop swelling from developing, and can be taken straight after an injury, shock or exhaustion. They are increasingly popular with women in labour as they help to reduce inflammation and bruising. Arnica ointment or lotion can be used for the relief of muscular pains, sprains, bruising or stiffness, and can be used to reduce swelling that has already begun, for instance, in muscular rheumatism.

Arnica montana

REMEDY FINDER

Items shown in blue are Weleda anthroposophic medicines, others are homoeopathic. Some are only available from Weleda or a local pharmacy (differs in different countries).

ACCIDENTS For accident upset (Arnica 6X tablets) Shock, fear and panic after an accident (Aconite)

ACNE The face is red, dry and burning hot (Belladonna) Large infected spos on the face and back (Hepar sulph) Red, painful, itchy spots (Rhus tox)

ANXIETY A calming remedy to help you relax (Avena Sativa Comp drops) For occasional edginess brought about by everyday stress and strain (Fragador tablets)

APPETITE Continual craving or complete loss of appetite (Arsen alb)

BITES AND STINGS Nettle rash (Combudoron spray) Insect stings (Apis mel) Horse-fly bites (Hypericum)

BRUISING A soothing remedy to relieve sprains and bruises (Arnica ointment/lotion)

BURNS & SCALDS For minor burns and scalds (Combudoron lotion) Sunburn with redness, heat and throbbing (Belladonna lotion) Stinging burns and scalds (Urtica urens lotion)

CATARRH Congestion and inflammation (Catarrh cream) Relief of sinus congestion (Oleum Rhinals Drops) Early stages of cold with dry nasal catarrh. Nose blocked at night (Nux vom)

COLIC Teething troubles in infants (Chamomilla drops/granules)

CONSTIPATION Occasional constipation (Clairo Tea, Laxodoron tablets)

CONVALESCENCE A dietetic drink with tonic properties, helpful in convalescence. (Blackthorn elixir)

COLDS & FLU For feverish influenza (Aconitum) Feverishness, stuffiness and sneezing at onset of colds (Ferrum phos)

COUGHS To relieve irritating coughs (Cough elixir, a traditional herbal expectorant) Dry, irritating coughs (Herb and honey cough elixir)

CUTS cuts and grazes, minor wounds and abrasions (Calendolon ointment/lotion)

DIARRHOEA Stomach ache, occasional diarrhoea, nausea and stomach upsets (Melissa Comp drops) Holiday diarrhoea (Arsen alb)

FLATULENCE (Carbo Bet tablets)

HAEMORRHOIDS & PILES (Antimony ointment)

HANGOVER Too much food and drink. Headache with coldness and irritability. (Nux vom)

HAYFEVER Apply inside the nostrils. (Gencydo ointment)

HEADACHES & MIGRAINE A mineral remedy (Bidor or *Kephalodoron* 1% & 5% tablets) Migraine (Feverfew tablets/drops)

INDIGESTION (Carvon tablets, Digestodoron tablets)

MENOPAUSE Hot, red face. Dry vagina. (Belladonna).

MENSTRUATION IRREGULARITIES (Menodoron)

NAUSEA (Melissa Comp drops) Travel sickness (Cocculus)

PRE-MENSTRUAL TENSION Tired and lacking energy. Cold sweats. Breasts swollen and painful. (Calc. carb) Irritable and over-sensitive. Symptoms of cystitis (Causticum)

RHEUMATISM Aid to the symptomatic relief of muscular rheumatism. (Birch elixir) A soothing, warming remedy for relief of muscular rheumatic pain (Copper ointment) Rheumatic pain, stiffness, fibrositis, backache, cramp (Massage Balm with Arnica)

SLEEPLESSNESS Aids peaceful relaxtion after a stressful day (Avena Sative Comp drops) For the relief of sleeplessness (Malvae tea)

SORE THROATS For sore throats, colds and catarrh in throat and upper chest (Cinnabar/Pyrites tablets)

SPRAINS A soothing remedy to relieve sprains and bruises (Arnica ointment/lotion)

TOOTHACHE/TEETHING To relieve colicky pain and teething troubles in infants (Chamomilla drops/granules)

WARTS General remedy for warts (Thuja)

Calendula

Knowledge of calendula's healing properties has existed for centuries. Otherwise known as the *English* or *pot* marigold, it is traditionally one of the most used herbs. It has been shown to have antiseptic, anti-microbial and anti-inflammatory properties, yet is gentle enough to be used in products for babies or others with sensitive skin. It is most valued for soothing damaged or irritated skin, helping a wound to heal, as well as for burns, boils or use after surgery. It is also used for nappy rash, eczema or minor abrasions, and is available as an ointment or lotion.

Tests have shown that the extract from the fresh plant is far more effective than dried extract. Calendula products are therefore made from fresh plants, grown according to the methods of biodynamic agriculture. Extracts are made from all of the plant, and from the flowers alone, to suit different product uses.

Anthroposophical preparations

Combudoron

The two main ingredients of Combudoron are *Arnica montana,* famous for its anti-inflammatory properties, and *Urtica urens,* the common nettle. Combudoron is used for the relief of insect bites and stings, but also works well on minor burns, including sunburn. It is also useful to soothe minor rashes, such as nettle rash.

A tincture is made from the whole plant of *Arnica Montana.* Arnica is used to reduce the swelling and pain associated with insect bites or stings, or burns and rashes. Another tincture is also prepared from the nettle leaves only of *Urtica urens.* This is included in Combudoron on the principle of curing like with like. Thus, the minute doses of the very substance which causes the symptoms of nettle rash are used to treat it.

Specific quantities of both tinctures are carefully measured out into stainless steel containers. The mixture is allowed to stand overnight, tightly lidded. The mixture is then passed through a fine filter to produce a clear brownish liquid. A sample of this is submitted to the quality- control department for testing, before being packaged and labelled.

Bidor

Bidor (or *Kephalodoron*) is a mixture of iron (ferrous) sulphate, quartz (silica) and honey. It is used for the treatment of migraine and tension headaches, and the nausea that may accompany them. Bidor's action is directed at harmonizing the fundamental imbalance of the nervous and metabolic systems at the root of the headache. Bidor has none of the side effects which can accompany the use of painkillers and other conventional anti-migraine medication.

Passion flower
(Passiflora incarnata)

Balsamicum

Balsamicum *(or Heilsalbe)* ointment contains calendula (marigold), dog's mercury *(Mercurialis perennis)*, Peru balsam *(Myroxylon perui-ferum)*, and antimony *(stibium)*. It is used for the general treatment of wounds, particularly for poorly healing wounds and infected spots and boils. It can also be used for treating some types of eczema and dermatitis.

Avena sativa comp.

This is a mixture of common valerian *(Valeriana offici-nalis)*, passion flower *(Passi-flora incarnata)*, hops, oats and a high homeopathic potency of coffee. It is used diluted in water, as an anti-dote to insomnia, particularly when caused by restlessness or nervous tension.

ACHIEVEMENTS

In infancy the human organism is more open and receptive to the kind of medicinal intervention that anthroposophical medicine offers. The perspectives that anthroposophical medicine brings to paediatric issues make a significant contribution, particularly in schools, where anthroposophical doctors work in collaboration with teachers. Examples here include vaccination, childhood illnesses, the treatment of fevers, and a different understanding of the role of education in promoting health and illness. Teachers sometimes request a visit from an anthroposophical doctor for children who are displaying behavioural problems. The doctor can suggest certain activities to help the children become more balanced, and in some cases will refer them for a particular therapy.

The contributions of anthroposophical medicine, though not yet generally recognized, are very significant in the prevention and treatment of cancer. Viscum preparations play an important part here (see page 50). The understanding of psychiatric conditions is another area of achievement, as well as the use of substances in the form of external compresses, special applications and so on for a large spectrum of conditions, particularly where there is a degenerative component. Common conditions such as migraines, influenza, sciatica, and indigestion are also amenable to anthroposophical treatment, and there is a range of over the counter medicines to treat conditions of this kind.

Anthroposophical medical establishments

Currently, just under two thousand anthroposophical doctors work in a variety of practices and hospitals in Europe and throughout the world. They are supported by hundreds of specially trained therapists and counsellors. Worldwide, the number of patients currently receiving anthroposophical medical treatment is approximately five million a year. In Great Britain, anthroposophical doctors work both within the NHS and in private practice.

FURTHER READING

*Books marked thus * require a well-developed understanding of anthroposophy.*

About anthroposophy

Childs, Gilbert, *Rudolf Steiner: his Life and Work,* Floris Books, Edinburgh 2003.

Lissau, Rudi, *Rudolf Steiner: Life, Work, Inner Path and Social Initiatives,* Hawthorn Press.

Steiner, Rudolf, *Occult Science,* Rudolf Steiner Press, London.

—, *Knowledge of the Higher Worlds,* Rudolf Steiner Press, London.

Anthroposophical medicine

Bie, Guus van der and Machteld Huber (eds.) *Foundations of Anthroposophical Medicine,* Floris Books, Edinburgh 2003.*

Evans, Michael, and Iain Rodger, *Healing for Body, Soul and Spirit: An Introduction to Anthroposophical Medicine,* Floris Books, 2000.

Steiner, Rudolf and Ita Wegman, *Fundamentals of Therapy,* Rudolf Steiner Press, London.*

Twentyman, Ralph, *The Science and Art of Healing,* Floris Books, Edinburgh. Homeopathic and anthroposophical insights into the science and art of healing with a historical and mythological background.

Individual development

Brink, Margaret van der, *More Precious than Light,* Hawthorn Press, Stroud 1994.

Floride, Athys, *Human Encounters and Karma*, Anthroposophic Press, New York 1983.

Lefebure, Marcus and Hans Schauder, *Conversations on Counselling between a doctor and a priest,* T & T Clark, Edinburgh 1982.

Jewell, Albert, *Spirituality and Ageing,* Jessica Kingsley Publishers, London.

Lievegoed, Bernard, *Man on the Threshold,* Hawthorn Press, Stroud.
—, *Phases: Crisis and Development in the Individual,* Rudolf Steiner Press, London.
Steiner, Rudolf, *Psychoanalysis and Spiritual Psychology,* Anthroposophic Press, New York 1990.
Treichler, Rudolf, *Soulways,* Hawthorn Press, Stroud.

Child-care, parenting

Glöckler, Michaela and Wolfgang Goebel, *A Guide to Child Health,* Floris Books, Edinburgh.
Lievegoed, Bernard, *Phases of Childhood,* Floris Books, Edinburgh.
Salter, Joan, *The Incarnating Child,* Hawthorn Press, Stroud.
—, *Mothering with Soul,* Hawthorn Press, Stroud.

Therapies

Denjean-von Stryk, Barbara and Dietrich von Bonin, *Anthroposophical Therapeutic Speech,* Floris Books, Edinburgh 2003.*
Hauschka, Margarethe, *Fundamentals of Artistic Therapy,* Rudolf Steiner Press, London.*
—, *Rhythmical Massage,* Mercury Press, New York.*
Kirchner-Bockholt, Margarete, *Foundations of Curative Eurythmy,* Floris Books, Edinburgh 2004.*
Mees-Cristeller, Eva, *The Practice of Artistic Therapy,* Mercury Press, Spring Valley, NY.*
Müller, Heinz, *Healing Forces in the Word and its Rhythms,* Kolisko Archive Publications, Ringwood 1983.
Poplawski, Thomas, *Eurythmy: Rhythm, Dance and Soul,* Floris Books, 1998.
Steiner, Rudolf, *Speech and Drama,* Rudolf Steiner Press, London.

Remedies

Wolff, Otto, *Home Remedies: Herbal and Homeopathic Treatments for use at Home,* Floris Books, 2000. An overview of remedies.

CONTACT ADDRESSES

Anthroposophical Clinics and Practitioners' Associations

Great Britain
Park Attwood Clinic
Trimpley, Bewdley DY12 1RE
Tel. 01299 861 444 Fax 01299-861 375

Raphael Medical Centre
Rehabilitation and Nursing Home
Hollanden Park, Coldharbour Lane
Hildenborough, Tonbridge TN11 9LE

General Practioners:
A current list can be found on
www.weleda.co.uk/antdoc.htm

United States
*Physicians' Association for Anthropo-
sophical Medicine (PAAM)*
123 Geddes Avenue,
Ann Arbor MI 48104-1797
Tel. 734-930-9462 Fax 734-662-1727
Email: paam@anthropsophy.org
www.paam.net

Canada
Canadian Anthropsophical Medical Ass.
Kenneth McAlister, MD
9100 Bathurst Street, Suite #2
Thornhill, Ont. L4J 8C7
Tel. 905-882-4949 Fax 905-882-0560
Email: dr.k.mcs@home.com

Australia
*Australian Anthroposophical Medical
Ass. Inc.*
Dr Antony Underwood
Suite 2, level 2 Gordon Centre, 802
Pacific Highway, Gordon NSW 2072
Tel. 02-9418 1388 Fax 02-9418 1418
Email: aunderwood@bigpond.com

New Zealand
*New Zealand Association of Anthropo-
sophical Doctors*
Dr Roger Leitch, 11 Woodford Road,
Mount Eden, Auckland 1103
Tel. 09-631 0477 Fax 09-843 3090
Email: rleitch@titan.co.nz
*www.anthroposophy.org.nz/Sections/
Medical/Associations/NZAAD/NZAAD.htm*

South Africa
Anthroposophical Medical Association, SA
Dr Raoul Goldberg
PO Box 760, Howard Place 7450
Tel/Fax 021-531 5766

Manufacturers of Anthroposophical Medicines

Great Britain
Weleda UK
Heanor Road, Ilkeston DE7 8DR
Tel. 0115-944 8200
Fax 0115-944 8210
Email: Info@Weleda.co.uk
www.weleda.co.uk

United States of America
Weleda Inc
PO Box 249, Congers NY 10920
Tel. 914-268 8572 Fax 914-268 8574
Email: Info@Weleda.com

Canada
Purity Life Health Products Ltd
6 Commerce Cres, Acton, Ont. L7J 2X3
Tel. 519-853 3511 / 800-265-2615
Fax 519-853 4660 / 800-930 9512
Email: info@puritylife.com
www.puritylife.com

Ireland
Weleda (Ireland) Ltd
Scoughan, Blessington, Co. Wicklow
Tel. 045-865 575 Fax 045-865 827
New Zealand
Weleda New Zealand
PO Box 8132, 302 Te Mata Road,
Havelock North
Tel. 06-877 7394 Fax 06-877 4989
Email: help@weleda.co.nz
www.weleda.co.nz

Australia
Weleda Pty Ltd
c/o Weleda New Zealand
Tel. 03-9723 7278 Fax +64-6-877 4989

South Africa
Weleda South Africa
(Division of Pharma-Natura Ltd)
PO Box 5502, Johannesburg 2000
Tel. 011-445 6016 Fax 011-445 6113
Email: eleanor@pharma.co.za

Acknowledgments

The author would like to thank the following for their help and contributions:
Frances Bay, James Dyson, Helen Frost, Aoine Landweer-Cooke, John Logan,
Donald Philips, John Playfoot, Don Ratcliffe, Fiona Sim, Andrea Sprenger.

Photographs:
Biodynamic Association 44; Ursula Browning 27, 35; Marga Hogenboom 21, 30, 31,
32, 35; Park Attwood Clinic 18, 29, 37; St Luke's Medical Centre, Stroud 23; Weleda
UK (Susie Fairgrieve) 2, 47, 51, 52, 53, 56, 58.